SUPERDOODLES
REPTILES
WRITTEN AND ILLUSTRATED BY BEV ARMSTRONG
The Learning Works

Editing and Typography by
Kimberley A. Clark

ISBN 0-590-99648-7

 Published by Scholastic Inc., 555 Broadway, New York, NY 10012, by arrangement with The Learning Works, Inc.

12 11 10 9 8 7 6 5 4 3 2 1 7 8 9/9 0 1 2/0

Printed in the U.S.A. 08
First Scholastic printing, September 1997

Introduction

SUPERDOODLES are books that provide easy, step-by-step instructions for super line drawings. The animals in this book may be sketched large for murals or posters, or small for bookmarks and flip books. They may be used individually in separate pictures or combined to create scenes of different habitats.

As you follow the steps, draw in pencil. Dotted lines appear in some steps. Make these lines light so that they can be easily erased later. If an animal has lots of stripes or spots, don't worry about copying the markings exactly—no two animals are identical. Finish your drawing by going over it with a colored pencil, crayon, or felt-tipped pen.

If you enjoy this book, look for other **Learning Works SUPERDOODLES.** Titles in this series are ***Dinosaurs***, ***Endangered Animals***, ***Mammals***, ***Marine Life***, ***Rain Forest***, ***Sports***, ***Vehicles***, and ***Zoo Animals***.

alligator snapper

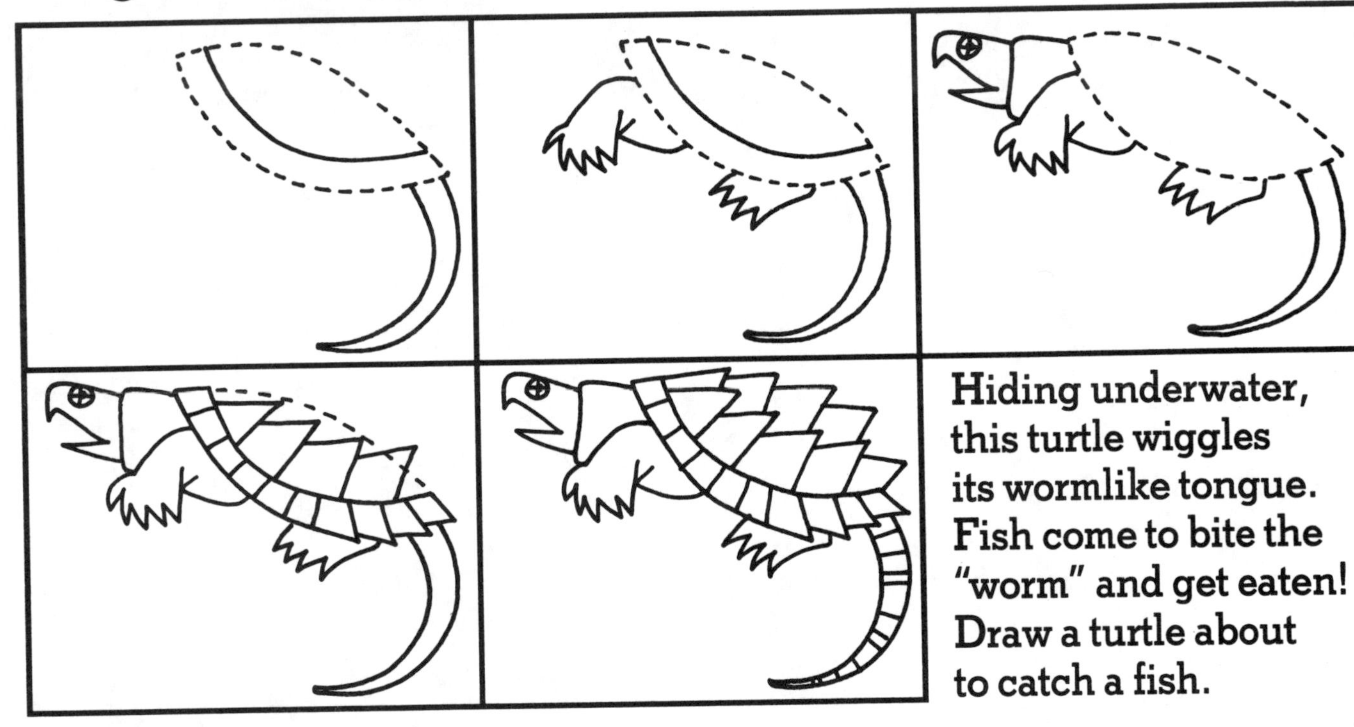

Hiding underwater, this turtle wiggles its wormlike tongue. Fish come to bite the "worm" and get eaten! Draw a turtle about to catch a fish.

ball python

When frightened, this snake rolls up into a tight ball. Make a bookmark with a picture of a relaxed, stretched-out python on it.

big-headed turtle

Turtles hatch from eggs that look like ping-pong balls. Draw a baby turtle peeking out through a crack in the shell of its egg.

box turtle

Box turtles like to eat snails, worms, and berries. Draw a box turtle finding something to eat.

Chinese alligator

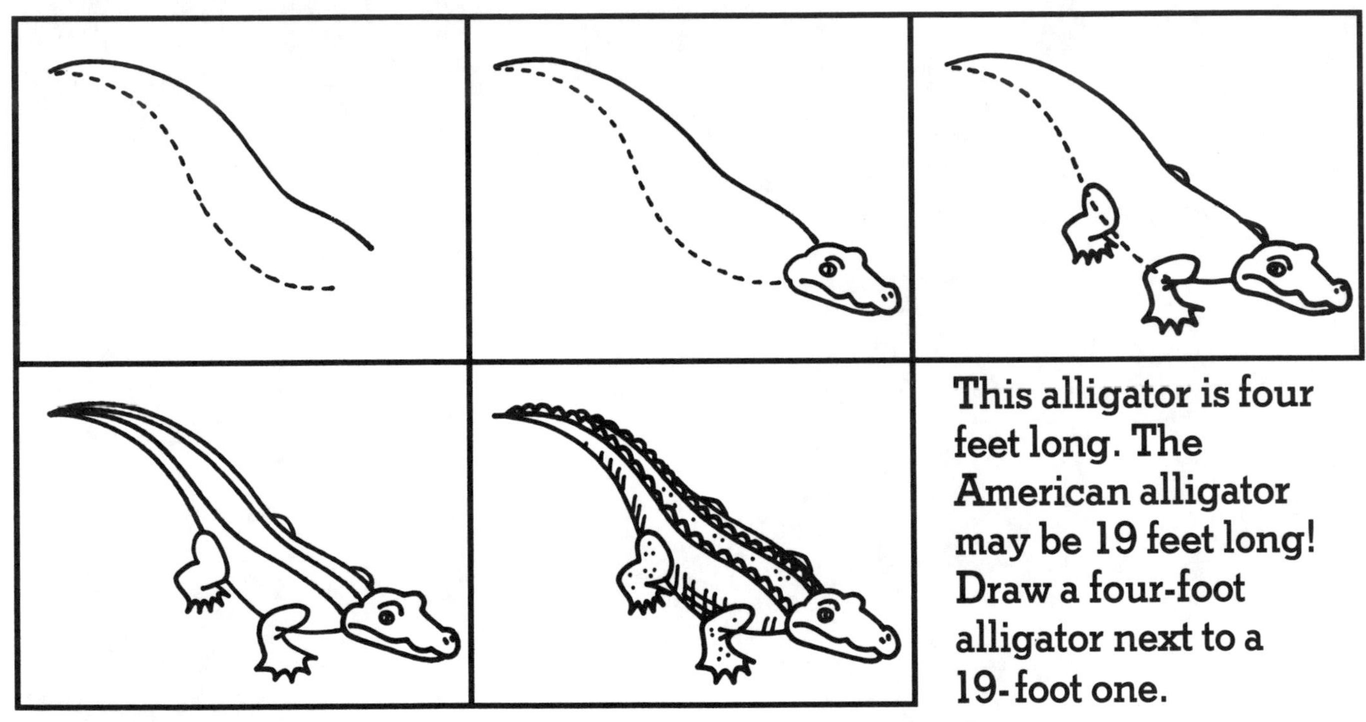

This alligator is four feet long. The American alligator may be 19 feet long! Draw a four-foot alligator next to a 19-foot one.

common chameleon

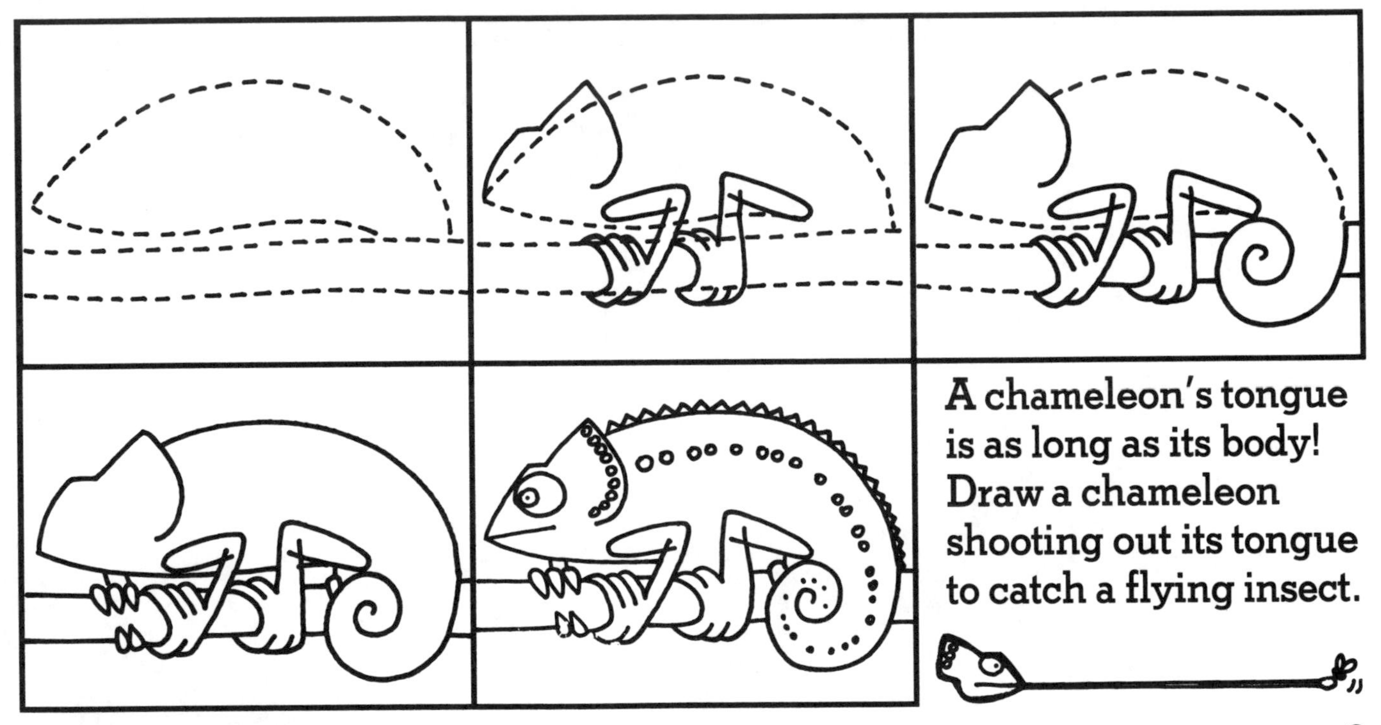

A chameleon's tongue is as long as its body! Draw a chameleon shooting out its tongue to catch a flying insect.

flying dragon

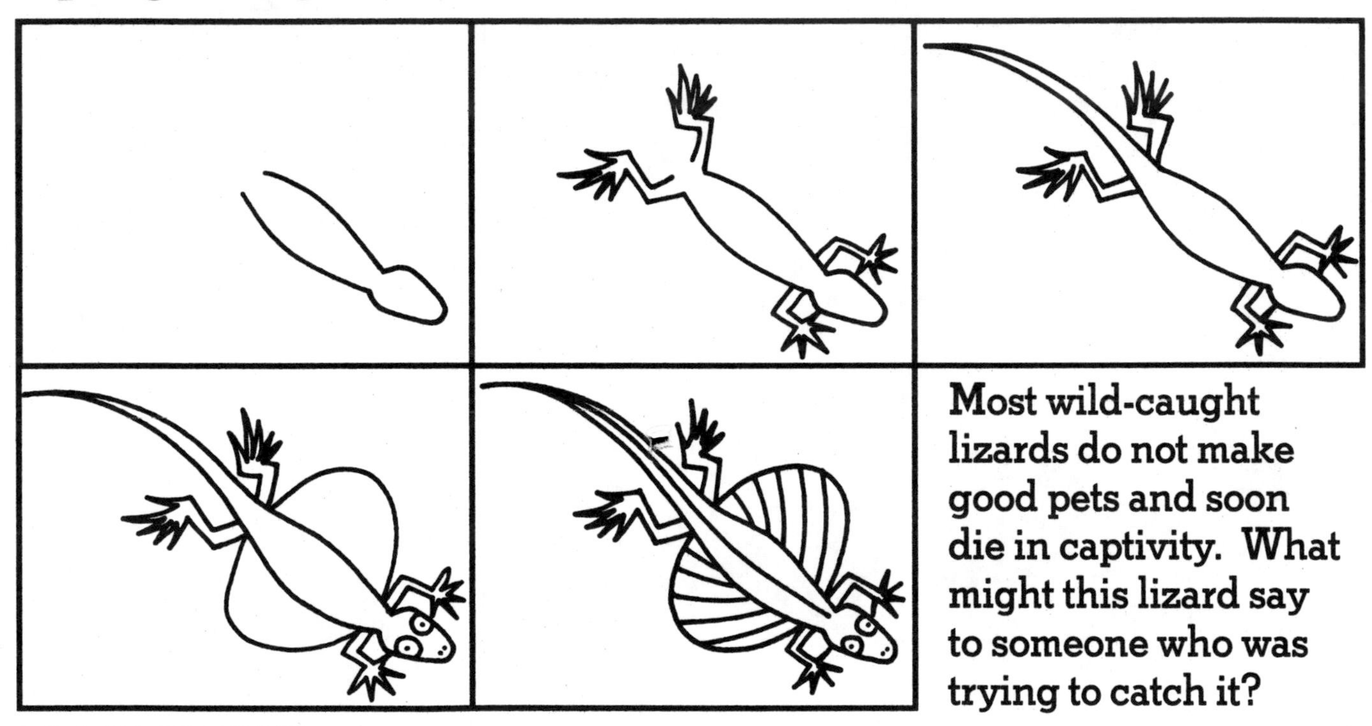

Most wild-caught lizards do not make good pets and soon die in captivity. What might this lizard say to someone who was trying to catch it?

frilled lizard

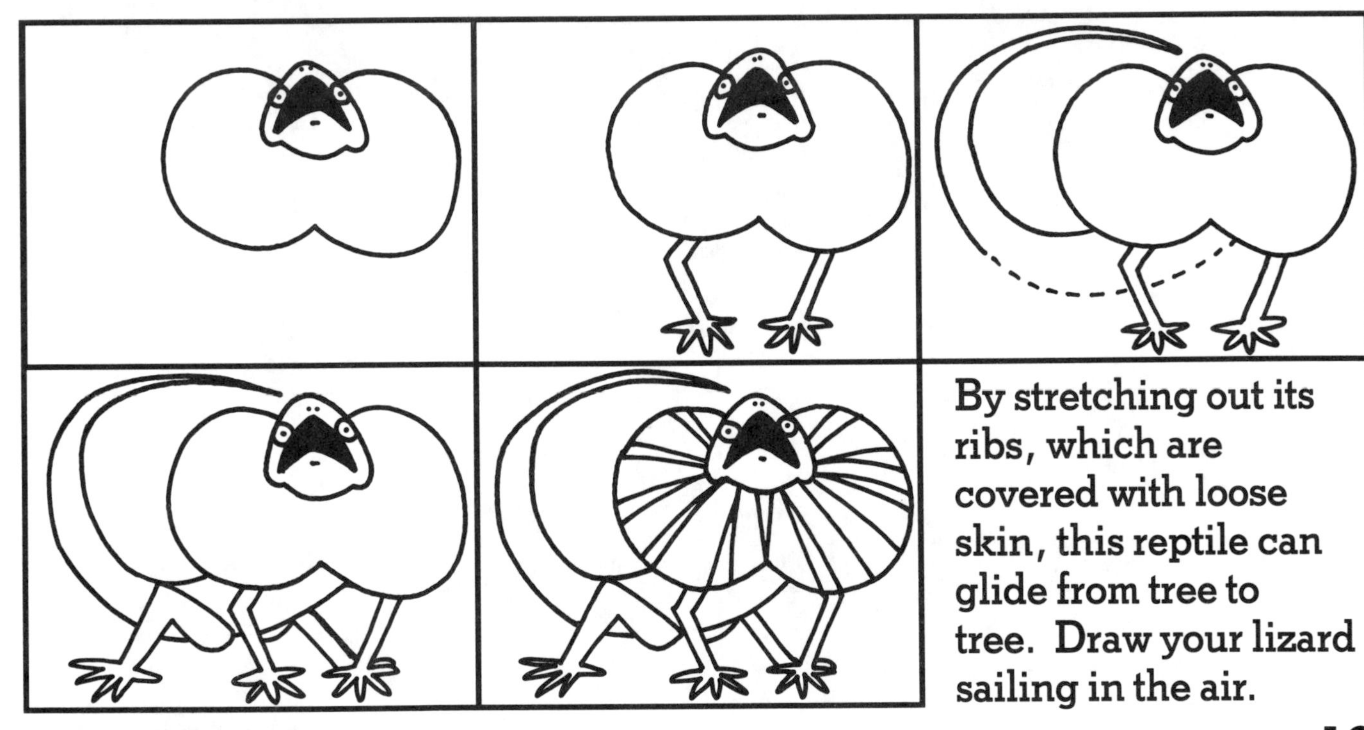

By stretching out its ribs, which are covered with loose skin, this reptile can glide from tree to tree. Draw your lizard sailing in the air.

Gaboon viper

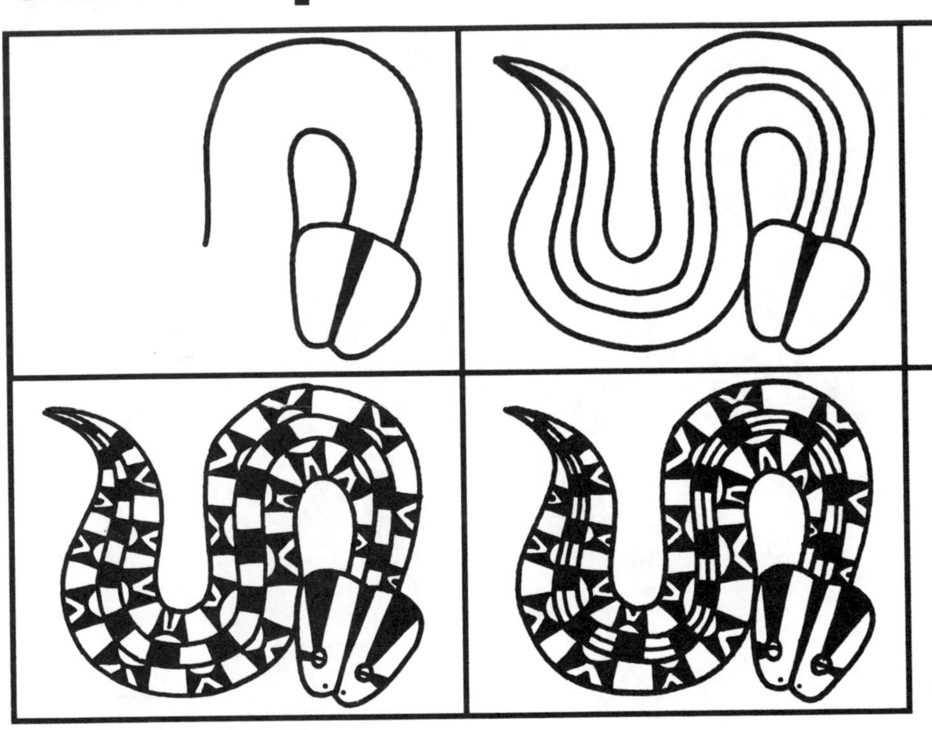

Although this snake has bold markings, it is very difficult to see when it is lying in dead leaves on the forest floor. Hide your snake in some leaves.

Galapagos tortoise

This tortoise may be three feet tall as it walks along. Draw yourself feeding a piece of fruit to the tortoise or scratching its chin.

gavial

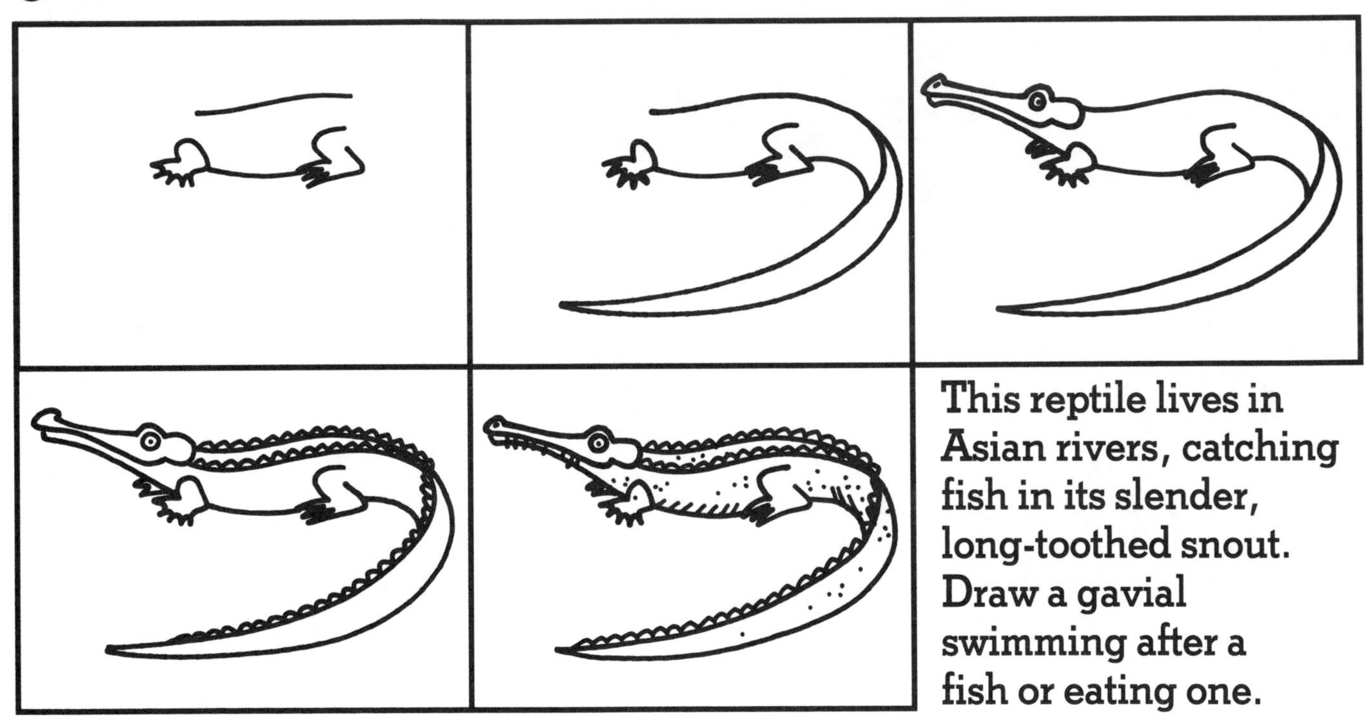

This reptile lives in Asian rivers, catching fish in its slender, long-toothed snout. Draw a gavial swimming after a fish or eating one.

Gila monster

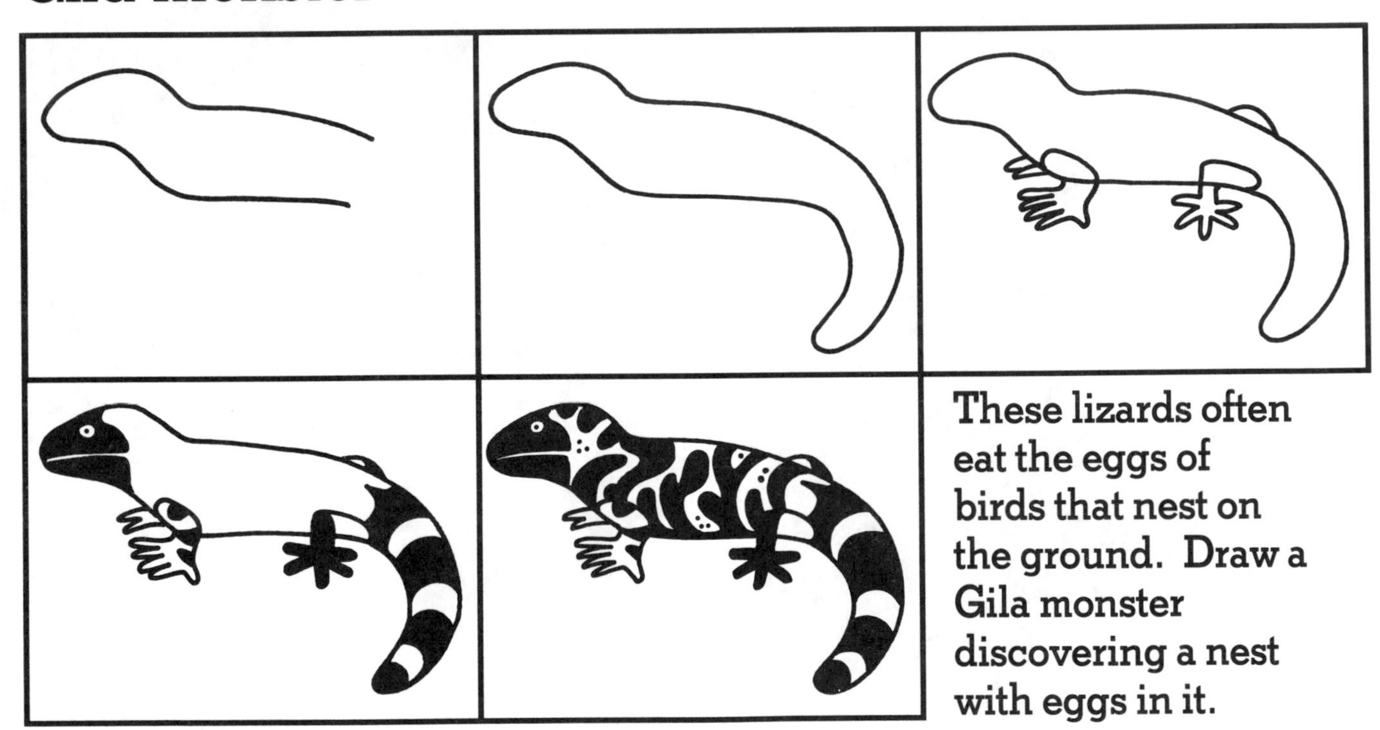

These lizards often eat the eggs of birds that nest on the ground. Draw a Gila monster discovering a nest with eggs in it.

green iguana

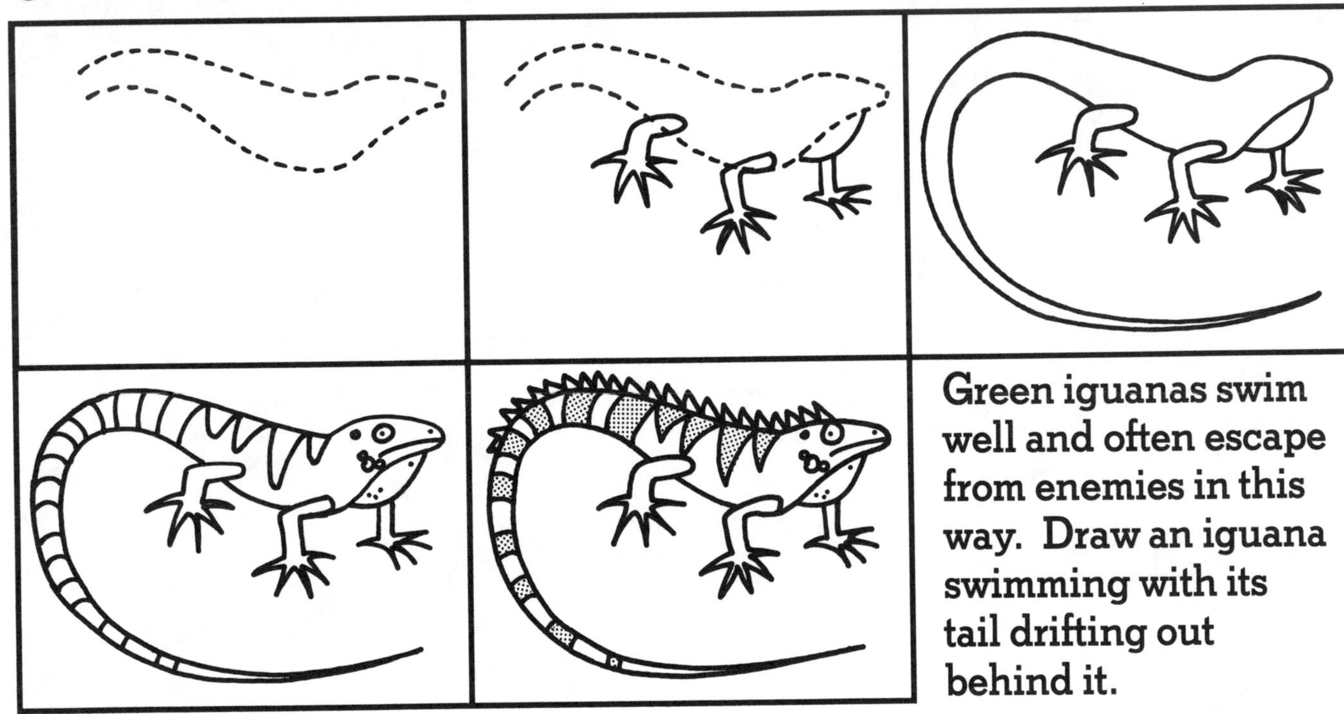

Green iguanas swim well and often escape from enemies in this way. Draw an iguana swimming with its tail drifting out behind it.

green tree python

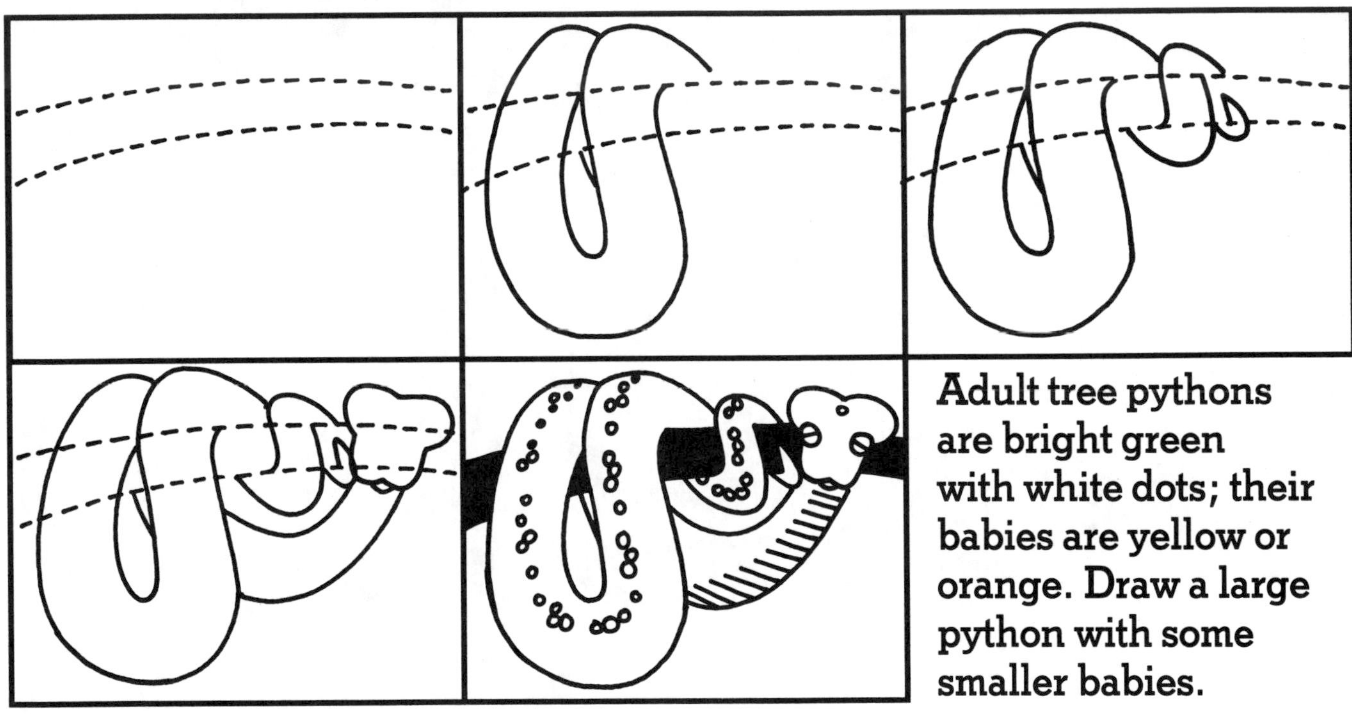

Adult tree pythons are bright green with white dots; their babies are yellow or orange. Draw a large python with some smaller babies.

hawksbill turtle

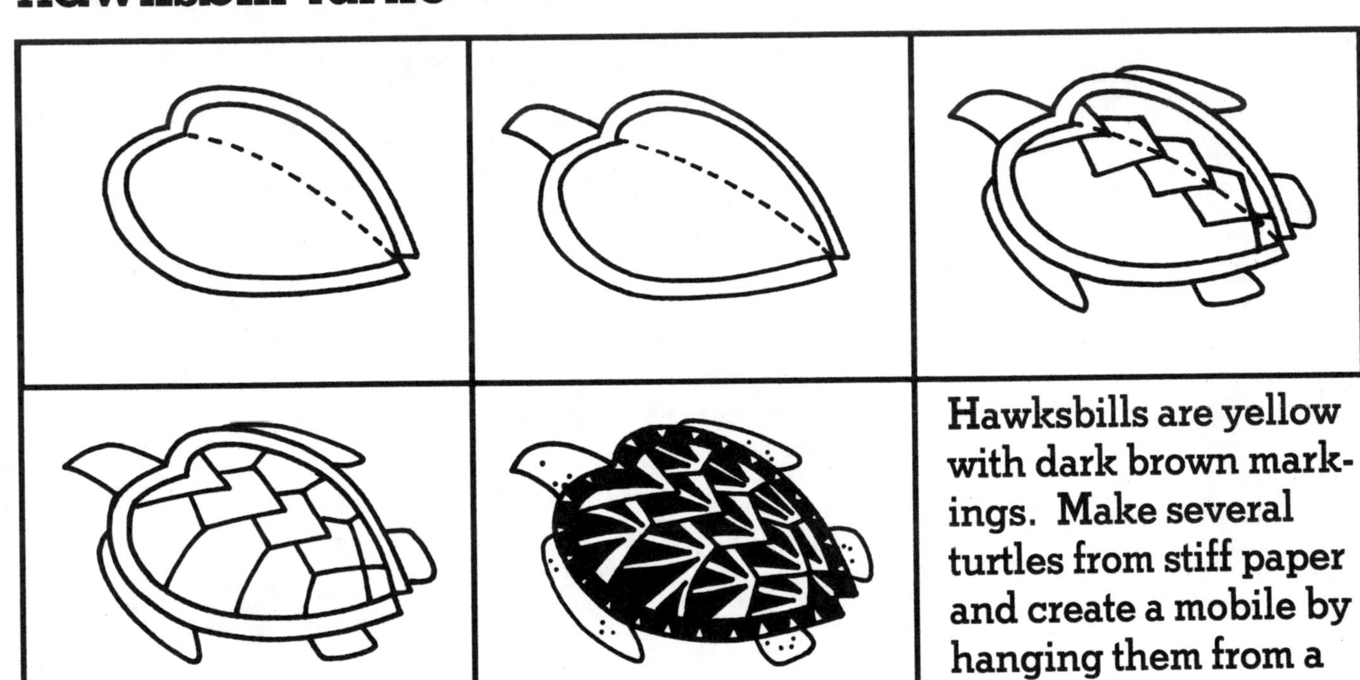

Hawksbills are yellow with dark brown markings. Make several turtles from stiff paper and create a mobile by hanging them from a stick or wire.

horned lizard

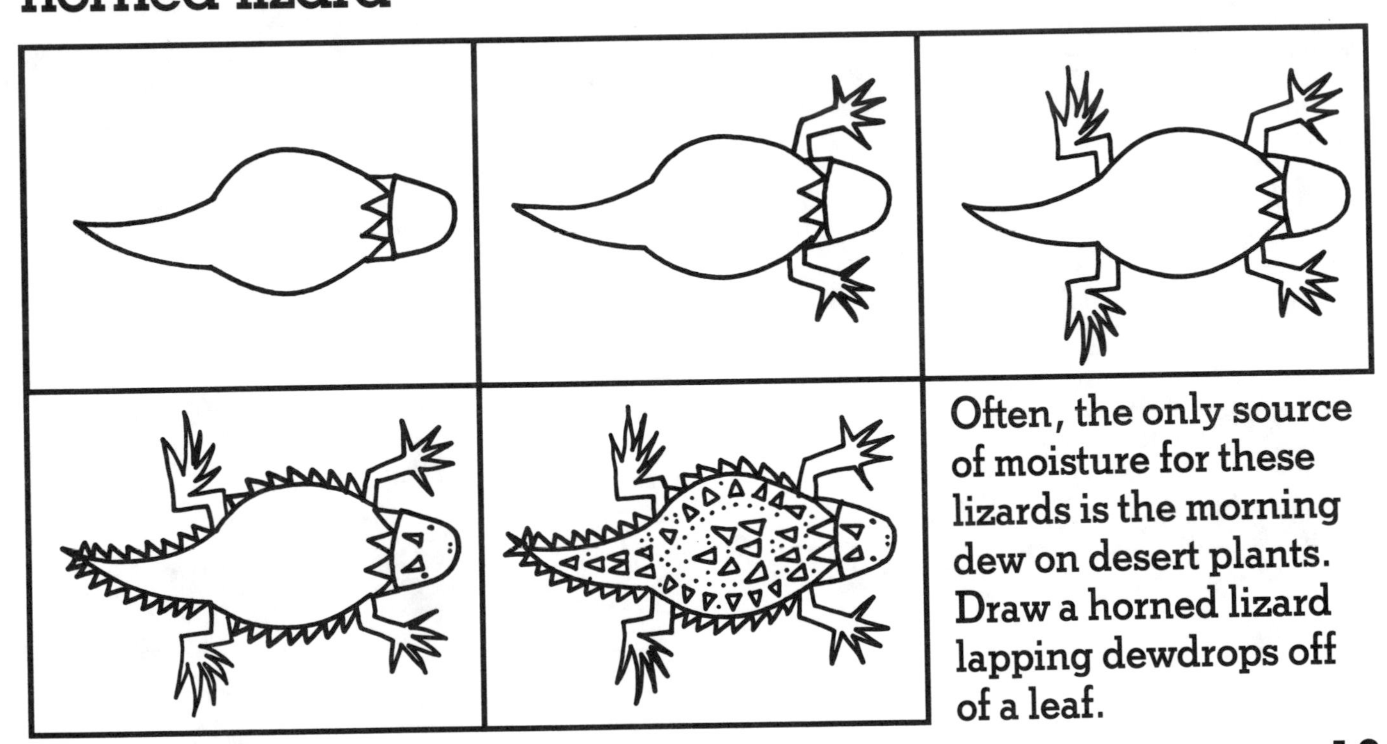

Often, the only source of moisture for these lizards is the morning dew on desert plants. Draw a horned lizard lapping dewdrops off of a leaf.

Indian cobra

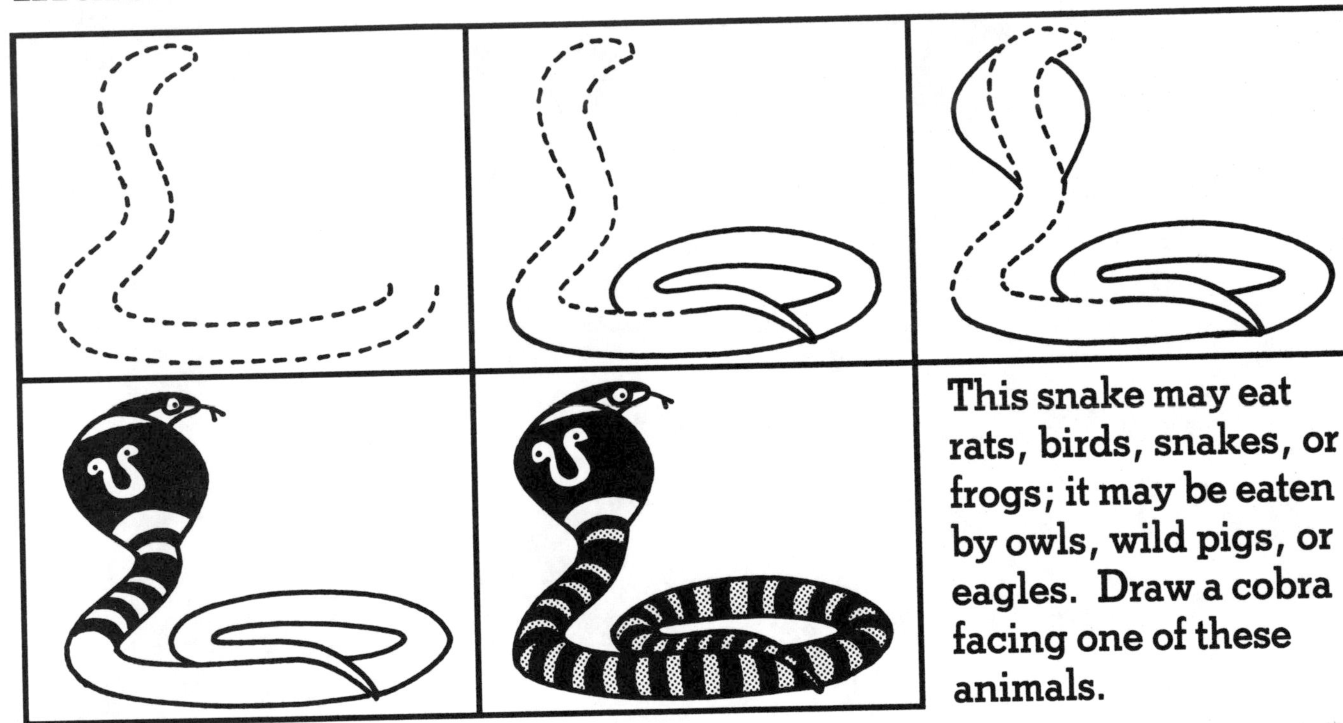

This snake may eat rats, birds, snakes, or frogs; it may be eaten by owls, wild pigs, or eagles. Draw a cobra facing one of these animals.

Mandarin ratsnake

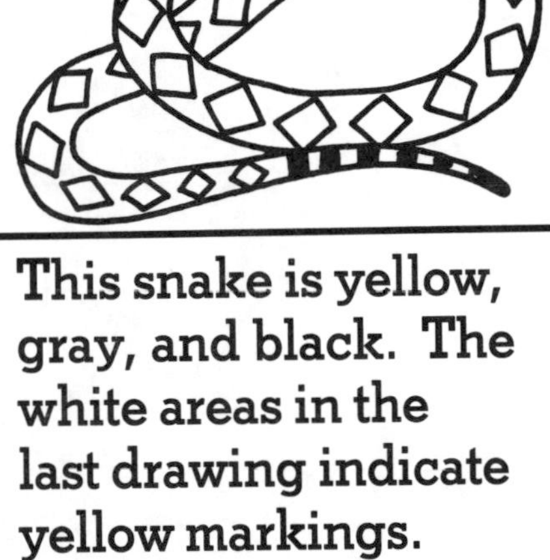

This snake is yellow, gray, and black. The white areas in the last drawing indicate yellow markings. Make a large colored drawing of this snake.

marine iguana

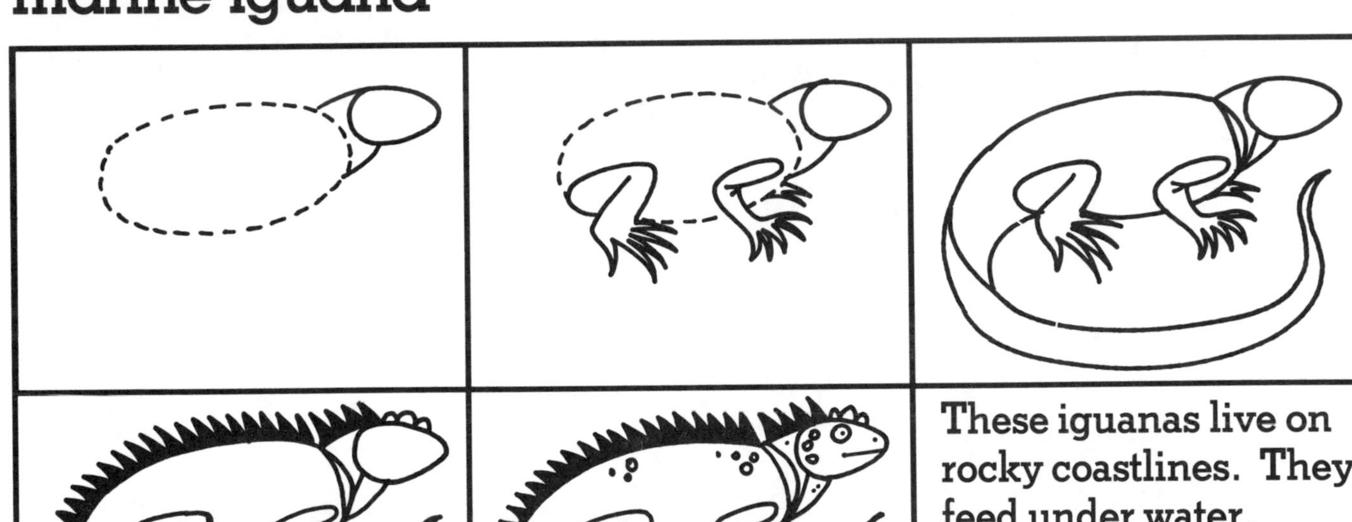

These iguanas live on rocky coastlines. They feed under water, eating seaweed that grows on the rocks. Draw an iguana diving for its dinner.

massasauga

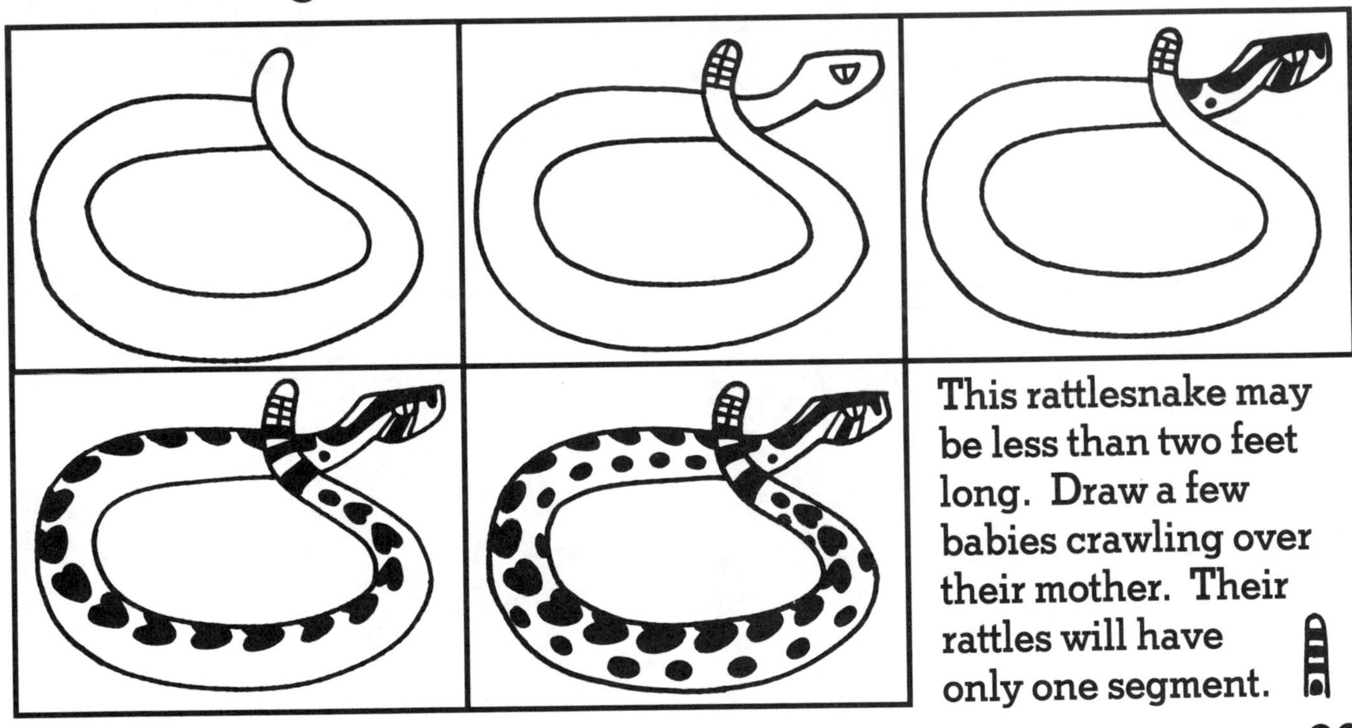

This rattlesnake may be less than two feet long. Draw a few babies crawling over their mother. Their rattles will have only one segment.

mata mata

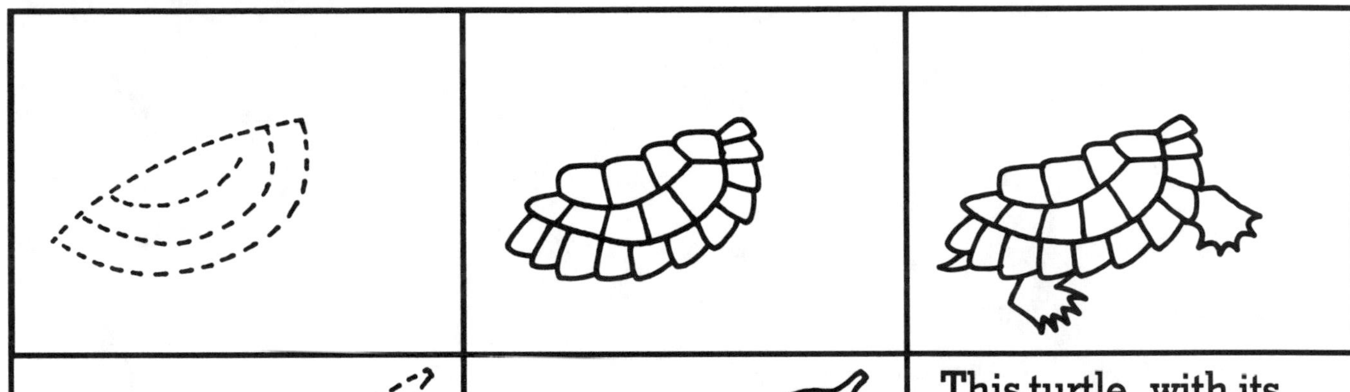

This turtle, with its loose, warty skin and algae-covered shell, looks very old and may even appear dead as it sits in muddy ponds. Draw a mata mata "at home."

monkey-tail skink

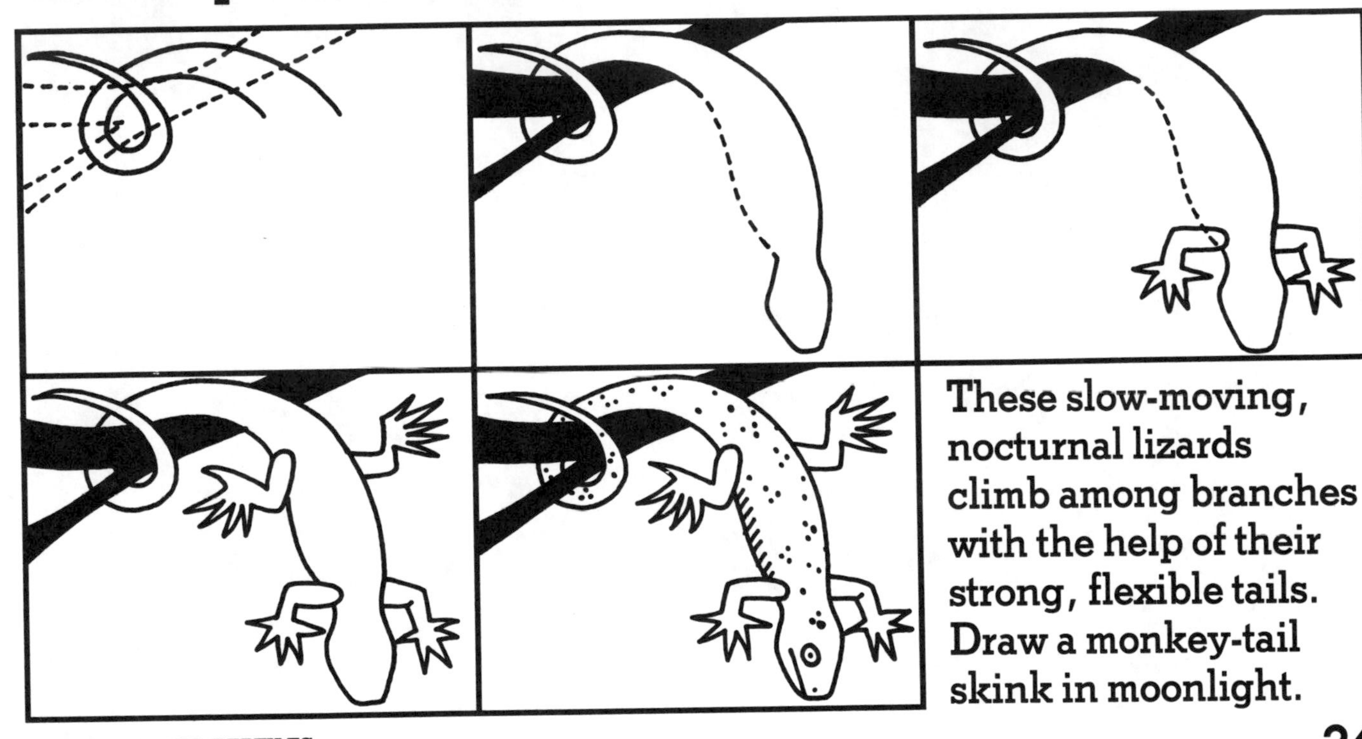

These slow-moving, nocturnal lizards climb among branches with the help of their strong, flexible tails. Draw a monkey-tail skink in moonlight.

pancake tortoise

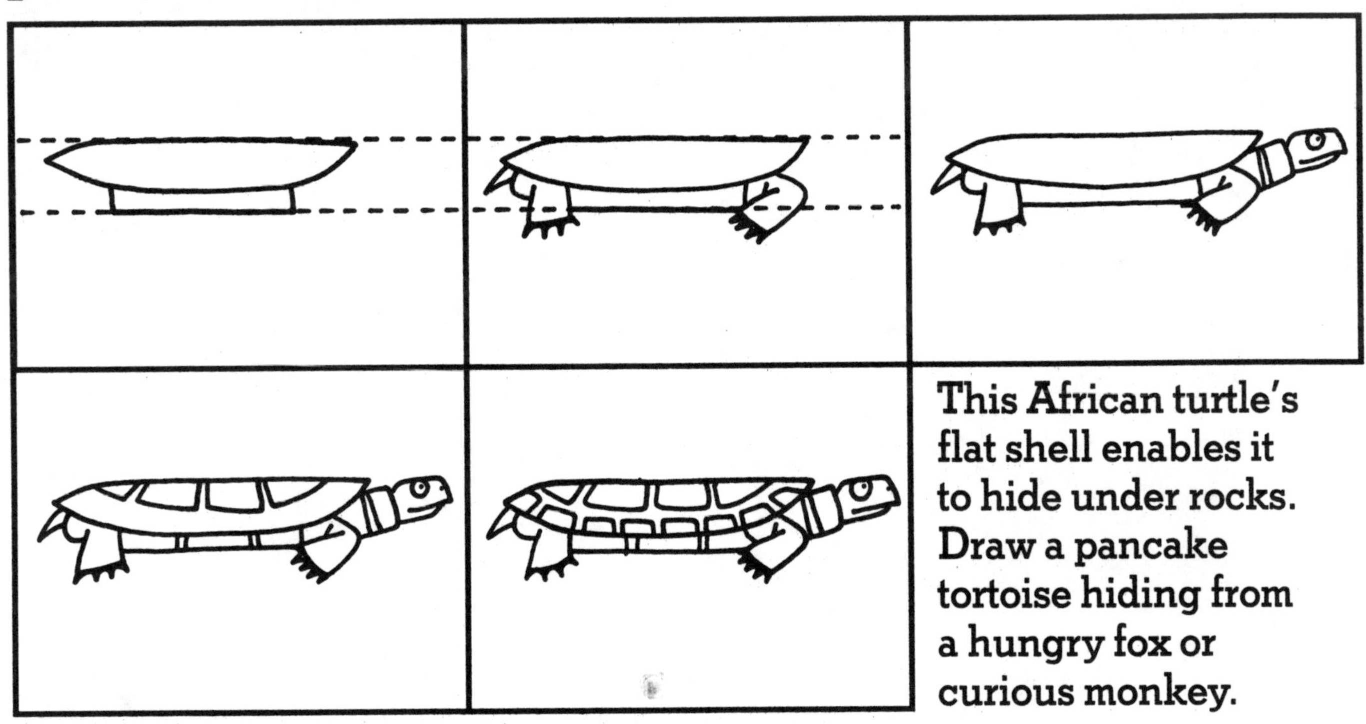

This African turtle's flat shell enables it to hide under rocks. Draw a pancake tortoise hiding from a hungry fox or curious monkey.

red-eared slider

Draw a long row of red-eared sliders sunning themselves on a log in a pond. Add cattails, dragonflies, and a swimming snake to the scene.

sand goanna

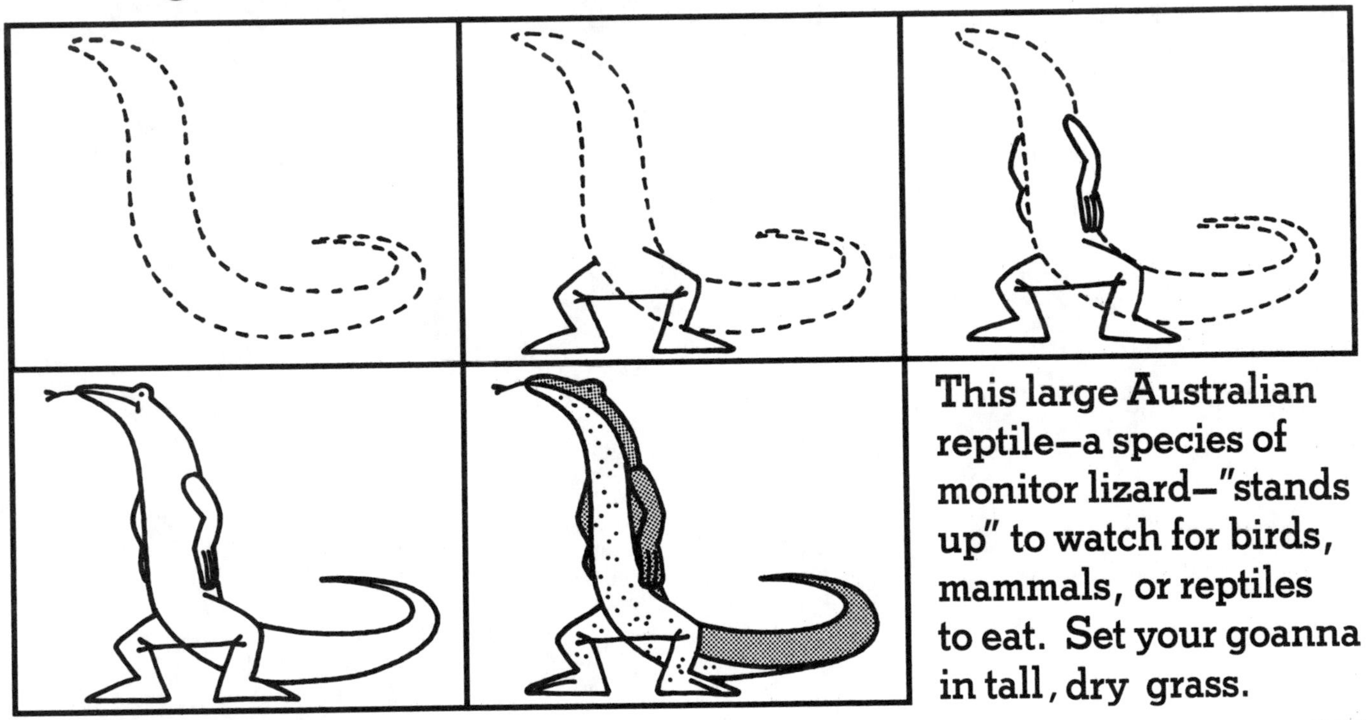

This large Australian reptile—a species of monitor lizard—"stands up" to watch for birds, mammals, or reptiles to eat. Set your goanna in tall, dry grass.

scarlet king snake

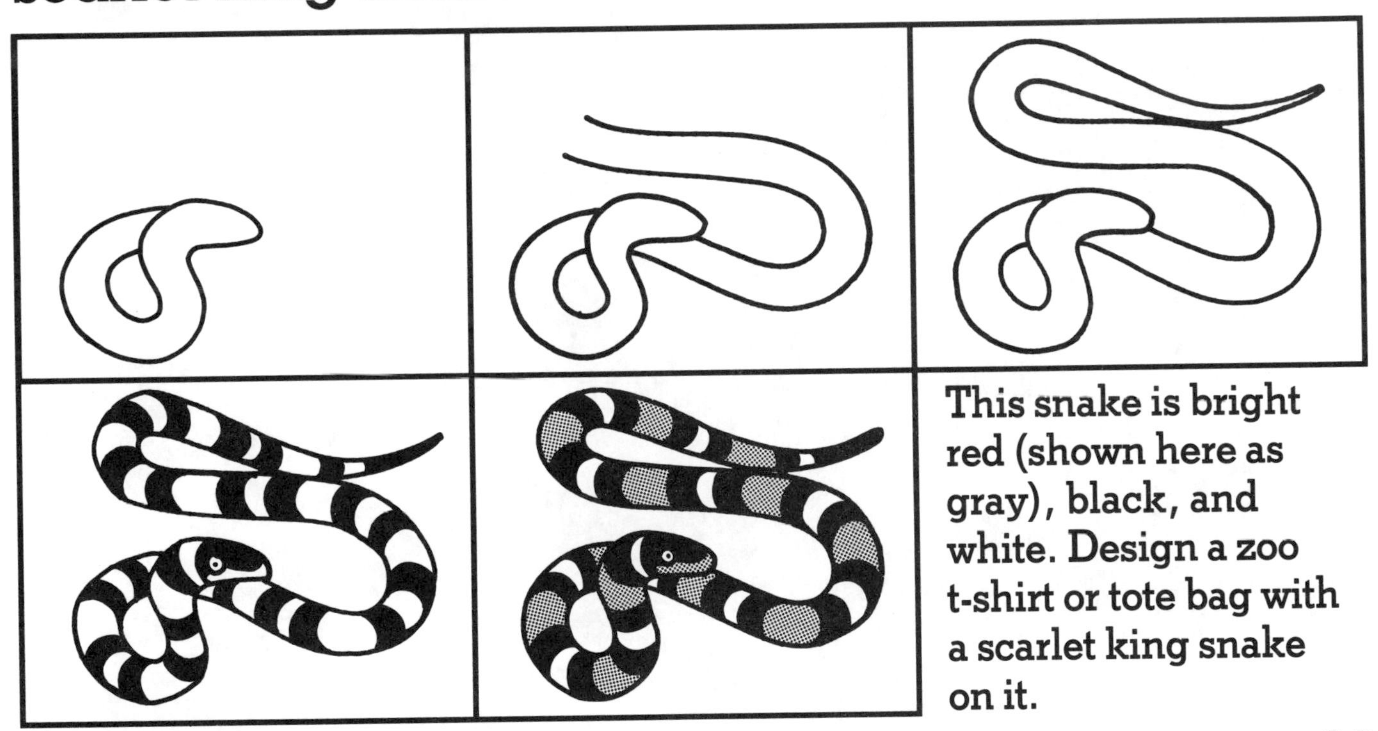

This snake is bright red (shown here as gray), black, and white. Design a zoo t-shirt or tote bag with a scarlet king snake on it.

shingleback

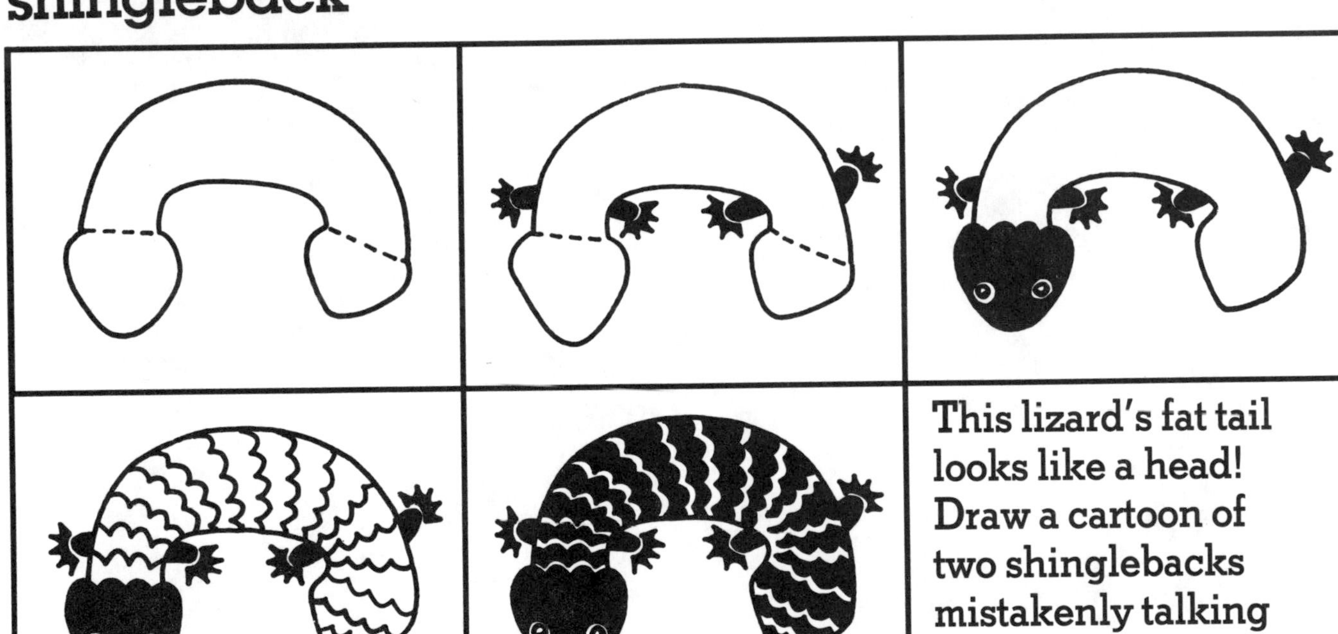

This lizard's fat tail looks like a head! Draw a cartoon of two shinglebacks mistakenly talking to each others' tails.

soft-shelled turtle

This turtle lives in shallow, mud-bottomed ponds, stretching its long neck so that its eyes and nose are above water. Put your turtle in a pond.

starred tortoise

This beautiful dark-brown-and-yellow tortoise is about ten inches long. Make a life-sized drawing of this reptile from India.

Tokay gecko

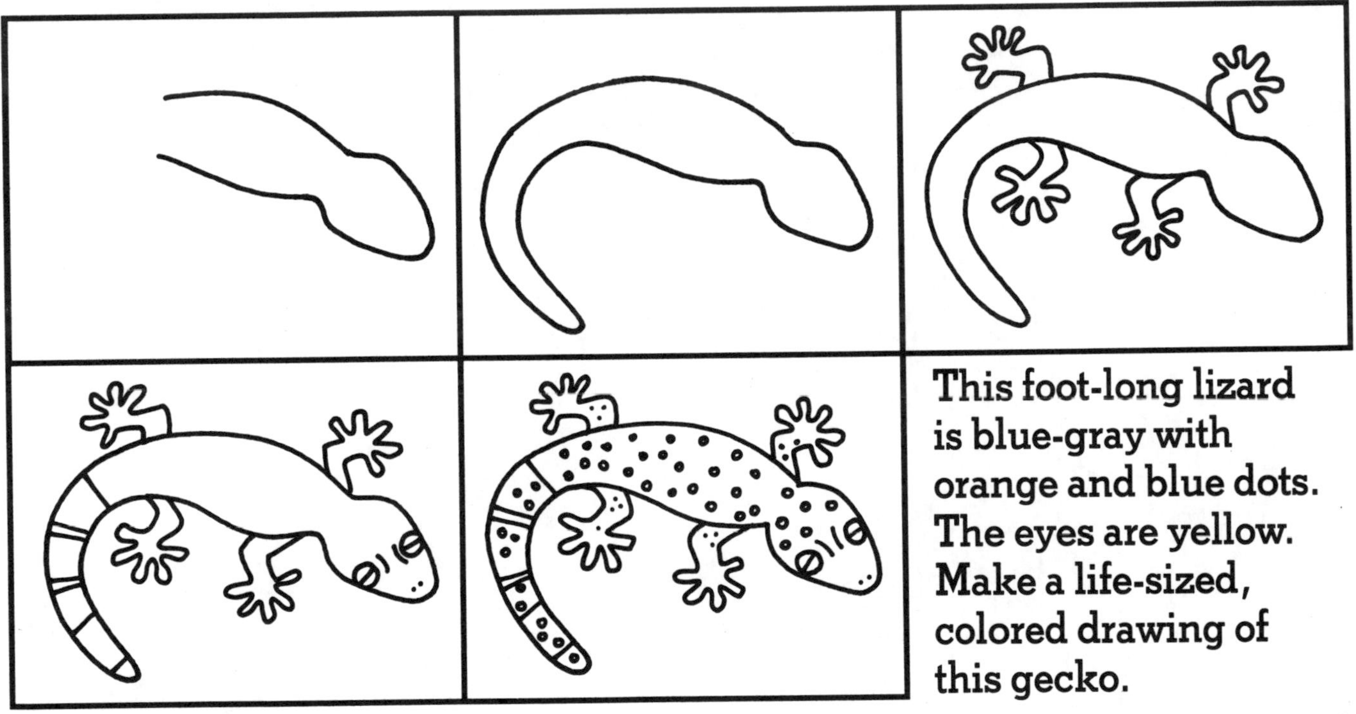

This foot-long lizard is blue-gray with orange and blue dots. The eyes are yellow. Make a life-sized, colored drawing of this gecko.